4.95

What Else Can I Pl
Trumpet
Grade Three

Series Editor: Mark Mumford

Music arranged and processed by
Barnes Music Engraving Ltd
East Sussex TN22 4HA, England

Published 1996

Introduction

In this *What Else Can I Play?* collection you'll find sixteen popular tunes that are both challenging and entertaining.

The pieces have been carefully selected and arranged to create ideal supplementary material for young trumpeters who are either working towards or have recently taken a Grade Three trumpet examination.

As the student progresses through the volume, technical demands increase and new concepts are introduced which reflect the requirements of the major Examination Boards. Suggestions and guidelines on breathing, dynamics and tempo are given for each piece, together with technical tips and performance notes.

Pupils will experience a wide variety of music, ranging from folk and classical through to showtunes and popular songs, leading to a greater awareness of musical styles.

Whether it's for light relief from examination preparation, or to reinforce the understanding of new concepts, this collection will enthuse and encourage all young trumpet players.

My funny valentine

Words by Lorenz Hart, Music by Richard Rodgers

The Rose of Tralee

Words by C Mordaunt Spencer, Music by Charles W Glover

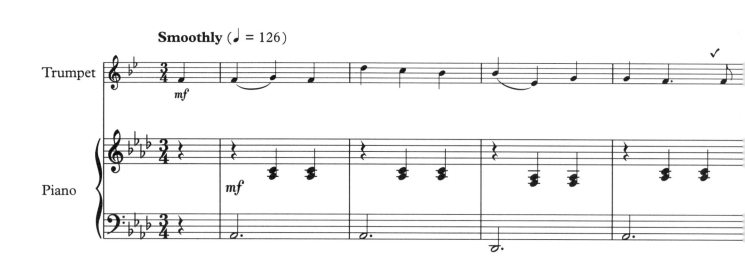

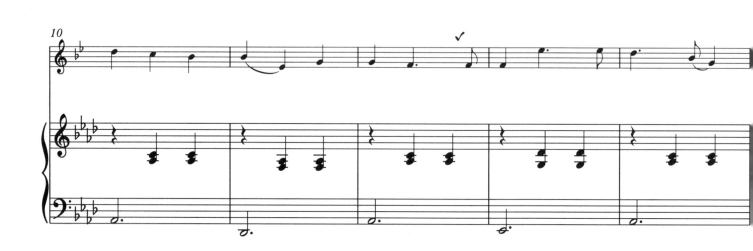

Bless yore beautiful hide

Words by Johnny Mercer, Music by Gene de Paul

September song

Words by Maxwell Anderson, Music by Kurt Weill

Forty-Second Street

Words by Al Dubin, Music by Harry Warren

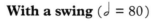

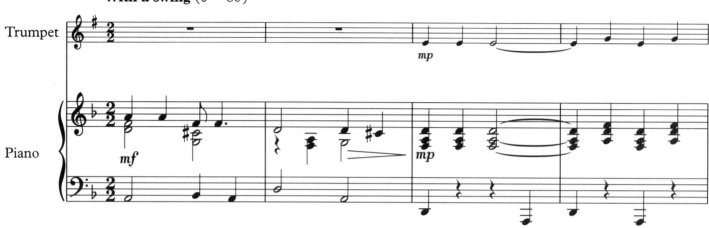

The shadow of your smile

Words by Paul Francis Webster, Music by Johnny Mandel

Consider yourself

Words and Music by Lionel Bart

What Else Can I Play?
Trumpet
Grade Three

My funny valentine

Words by Lorenz Hart, Music by Richard Rodgers

Between the years 1918 and 1942 the writing partnership of Richard Rodgers and Lorenz Hart produced a string of wonderful songs including such classics as 'Manhattan', 'Thou Swell', 'The Lady is a Tramp' and 'I Could Write a Book'. When Hart retired, Rodgers went on to further extraordinary success in his partnership with Oscar Hammerstein II.

Make sure you prepare yourself with big deep breaths in this piece to enable you to play through the phrases with a nice round tone and plenty of expression. Remember to project the sound well and to push it out using the diaphragm on the high notes. You will also need to support the airflow when playing the quieter lower notes.

The Rose of Tralee

Words by C Mordaunt Spencer, Music by Charles W Glover

Tralee is a town in Ireland, from where this ballad takes its name. This was one of many songs made popular after the Second World War by the ballad singer John McCormack.

Open up the sound to produce a full rich tone and soft-tongue the notes for smoothness. Give an extra push of air when aiming for the higher notes so that they don't sound flat.

Bless yore beautiful hide

Words by Johnny Mercer, Music by Gene de Paul

This song comes from the musical show *Seven Brides for Seven Brothers* (1954), a tale of American country folk in the 1850s. The film version, which starred Howard Keel and Jane Powell, won an award for the Best Scoring of a Musical Picture.

Careful use of all the dynamics and articulation will bring out the contrasts in this piece. Keep your playing light so the music doesn't drag. Avoid squeezing the top notes out – push more air through and broaden the tone.

September song

Words by Maxwell Anderson, Music by Kurt Weill

This song was written for the 1938 musical show *Knickerbocker Holiday* and has been recorded by Frank Sinatra and Bing Crosby. Composer Kurt Weill is particularly famous for his collaborations with the German playwright Bertolt Brecht, especially their stage musical *The Threepenny Opera* (1928).

You need a rich tone for this piece: think low and use a flat tongue position to open out for the lower notes. Space the triplets equally, taking care not to rush them. The low Ds and C sharps will sound sharp in relation to the surrounding notes, so try extending the third valve slide to compensate.

Forty-Second Street

Words by Al Dubin, Music by Harry Warren

This was the title song of the theatre musical and the film of 1932, and was sung by Dick Powell and Ruby Keeler as they danced on top of a taxi cab. The story was also used for another filmed musical from the same period, *The Gold Diggers of 1933*, for which songwriters Al Dubin and Harry Warren also wrote the music.

Observe all the stylistic markings and bring out the excitement in this piece. Practising chromatic scales will help the quaver passages run with ease. Always aim for the centre of the note so that you produce a good clear tone.

The shadow of your smile

Words by Paul Francis Webster, Music by Johnny Mandel

This song is from the film *The Sandpiper* (1965) which starred Richard Burton and Elizabeth Taylor. It won both the Academy Award for Best Song and a Grammy Award in the same year.

Play smoothly with a soft tongue, and don't forget to extend the third slide for the low C sharps. Try not to rush the quavers. Count your way through the long tied notes so you don't lose track of the beat. Make full use of the dynamics for maximum expression.

Consider yourself

Words and Music by Lionel Bart

Born in the East End of London in 1930, Lionel Bart is one of Britian's greatest popular composers and lyricists. With the long-running musical *Oliver!* from which this song comes, Bart helped the re-emergence of the British musical in 1960 after a long period of domination by Americans. The film version of *Oliver!* won six Oscars.

Play this piece rather cheekily. Shorten the notes a little to make them bounce along, remembering not to tongue-stop the notes. Take care with the accidentals and make sure you push the valves down cleanly, especially with the tricky fingering in the opening phrase.

Autumn leaves
(Les Feuilles Mortes)

English words by Johnny Mercer, French words by Jacques Prévert, Music by Joseph Kosma

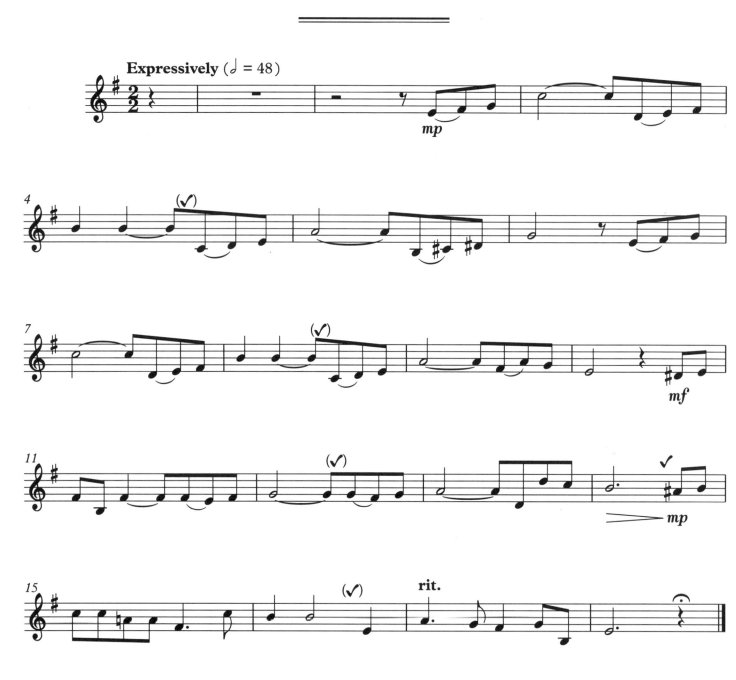

Jacques Prévert (1900–1977), who wrote the words of 'Les Feuilles Mortes', was one of France's most celebrated film-makers. He didn't start writing poetry until he was 46, but was soon placed as one of the greatest modern French poets too. Several of his poems have been set to music.

'Autumn Leaves' is a slow and beautiful piece, needing a rich warm tone. Sustain the long notes but always think in phrases to keep the melody flowing. Take care with the intervals and try to pitch each note in your head before you play it.

French words and music © 1947 & 1996 Enoch et Cie, France
English words © 1950 Ardmore Music Corp, France
Peter Maurice Music Co Ltd, London WC2H 0EA

Alexander's ragtime band

Words and Music by Irving Berlin

Irving Berlin swept the public off their feet with this piece, one of the greatest of all ragtime songs, which first appeared in 1911. Ragtime was a forerunner of jazz, precisely notated rather than improvised, which emerged right at the end of the nineteenth century and remained popular until the 1920s when improvised jazz took over.

Keep this piece moving along and try not to be late after the quaver rests. There are some tricky fingerings, especially in bar 14, which will benefit from being practised slowly until your fingers get used to them.

Speak softly love
(Love theme from 'The Godfather')

Words by Larry Kusik, Music by Nino Rota

This song was the love theme from Francis Ford Coppola's film *The Godfather* (1972) which starred Marlon Brando and Al Pacino. Composer Nino Rota won an Oscar for his score to the sequel, *The Godfather, Part II*.

Good breath control is needed here to support the airflow while you are playing softly. Try to glue all the notes together by playing long soft-tongued notes. You'll need to extend the third valve slide for the low Ds and C sharps so they don't sound too sharp.

Sunny afternoon

Words and Music by Ray Davies

This was a Number One hit for the Kinks in 1966, coming in the middle of a string of chart successes for the band over a period of seven years. The Kinks' style was typified by catchy tunes with clever and humorous lyrics which mocked conventional ideas of the time. Ray Davies is rated as having been one of Britain's finest songwriters during the 1960s.

Keep the rhythm bright and let this piece move along. Practise the octave slur in bar 21 on its own a few times until you can play it confidently. Try to project the sound at the end without forcing the tone.

Man of mystery

Michael Carr

This piece was a hit for the British instrumental group the Shadows in 1960. Having established themselves as the backing band to singer Cliff Richard in the early years of his career, the Shadows also had a string of hits in their own right, characterised by expert guitar playing and a distinctive melodic sound.

Control the sound carefully, especially when playing high notes quietly. Remember not to stretch your lips outwards, but imagine that you are pushing the corners inwards, supporting them by the flow of air. Play through the phrases and lean on the *tenuto* a little. Let the tone fade away to almost nothing at the end.

American patrol

F W Meacham

F. W. Meacham wrote this song in 1885 but it was adapted with added lyrics and popularised in the early 1940's. Glenn Miller's lively arrangement was a hit in 1941, but the piece was played by many other well-known artists too.

Short precise quavers and semiquavers will keep this piece lively without being played too fast. Remember to tongue the high G after the triplet in bar 33. Push the corners of the lips inwards to make them vibrate faster so that the notes sing out, supported by the airflow.

Over the rainbow

Words by E Y Harburg, Music by Harold Arlen

'Over the Rainbow' was written for the musical film *The Wizard of Oz*, which was released in 1939 and starred the legendary singer Judy Garland. Writer Harold Arlen (1905–1986) spent much time in Hollywood composing songs, including 'It's only a Paper Moon', 'Stormy Weather' and 'That Old Black Magic'.

Enjoy this lovely melody and bring it out as a singer would. Try to play right up to the ends of phrases, giving full value to all the notes, taking care to remember the key signature. Soft-tongue the notes to avoid any harsh attacks, especially when reaching for the high ones.

Soldiers' March
from 'Faust'

Charles Gounod

The French composer Charles Gounod lived from 1818 to 1893. His opera *Faust*, based on a much-altered version of Goethe's drama, was composed in 1859, the same year that Charles Darwin's *Origin of Species* was published.

There are some awkward fingerings in this piece, so keep the tempo steady. Make sure you place every note in exactly the right place by subdividing the bar into six quavers. Articulate all the unphrased quaver rhythmic patterns using a precise tongue attack and support the airflow with the diaphragm.

The Thunderer

John Philip Sousa

The American composer John Philip Sousa (1854–1932) was most famous for his military marches but was also known for his many operettas. His spirited marches inspired great patriotic feeling in the USA. He is quoted as having said 'a march should make a man with a wooden leg step out'!

In this piece there are some difficult intervals which may need some practice on their own at first. Remember to push from your diaphragm for the higher notes and open up the sound for all the notes so they sing out and do not sound strained. Play quavers lightly, even in loud passages, so that you can show off your tonguing expertise.

Printed by
Halstan & Co. Ltd., Amersham, Bucks., England

Autumn leaves
(Les Feuilles Mortes)

English words by Johnny Mercer, French words by Jacques Prévert, Music by Joseph Kosma

Alexander's ragtime band

Words and Music by Irving Berlin

Speak softly love
(Love theme from 'The Godfather')

Words by Larry Kusik, Music by Nino Rota

Expressively ($\quarternote = 72$)

Sunny afternoon

Words and Music by Ray Davies

Man of mystery

Michael Carr

American patrol

F W Meacham

Over the rainbow

Words by E Y Harburg, Music by Harold Arlen

Soldiers' March
from 'Faust'

Charles Gounod

The Thunderer

John Philip Sousa

Lightly (♩ = 120)

Printed by
Halstan & Co. Ltd., Amersham, Bucks., England